Bear Gets Dressed

A Guessing-Game Story

by Harriet Ziefert
pictures by Arnold Lobel

ABRAMS & COMPANY Publishers, Inc.

Early every morning Bear begins to dress.
What will he wear? See if you can guess.

Today it's very chilly. Bear is getting dressed. What will he wear? See if you can guess.

What a rainy day! Bear is getting dressed.
What will he wear? See if you can guess.

It's snowing outside. Bear is getting dressed.
What will he wear? See if you can guess.

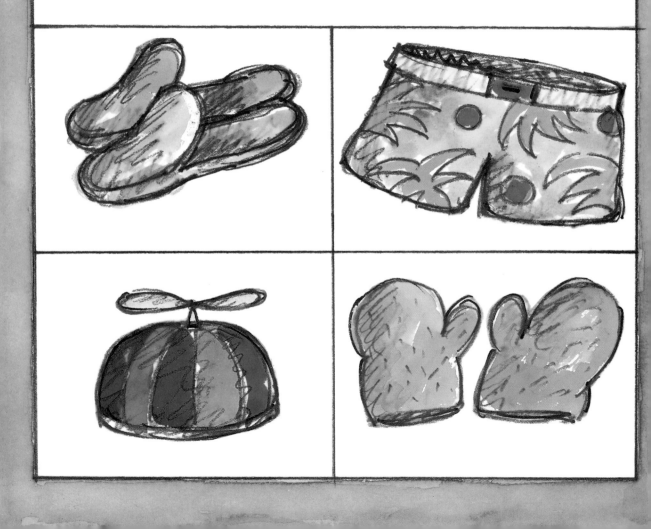

Today the sun is shining. Bear is getting dressed. What will he wear? See if you can guess.

What a windy day! Bear is getting dressed.
What will he wear? See if you can guess.

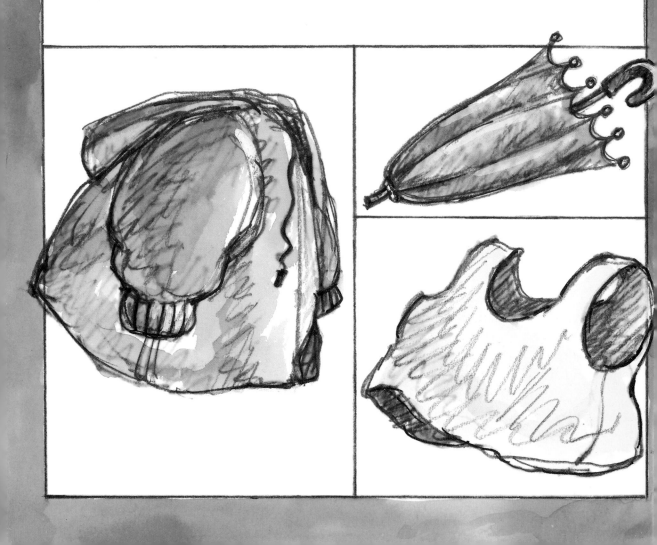

Early every evening Bear goes to bed.

Good night, Bear!